McGraw-Hill Reading WonderWorks

Unit 3
Decodable Reader

Mc Graw Hill Education

Bothell, WA • Chicago, IL • Columbus, OH • New York, NY

Contents

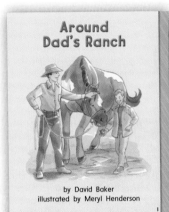

Around Dad's Ranch 1
Consonant Digraphs *ch, -tch, ph*

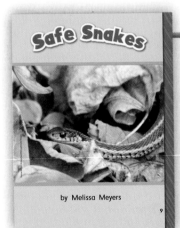

Safe Snakes 9
Long *a (a_e)*

by Camille Iglesias
illustrated by Anni Matsick

17

Time to Pick Up Together 17

Long *i (i_e)*

by Yeun Ho
illustrated by Deborah Colvin Borgo

25

A Spice Cake from Vance 25

Soft *c;* Soft *g*

by Akisha Owens
illustrated by Meryl Henderson

33

Steve's Huge Step 33

Long *o (o_e),* Long *u (u_e),*
Long *e (e_e)*

Around Dad's Ranch

by David Baker
illustrated by Meryl Henderson

This is Mitch.
Mitch's Dad has a ranch.
It is a big **place**.

Dad has a truck.
Dad has a van.
Mitch helps Dad hitch the van.
Many chicks peck in a pen.

Mitch and Dad will go out.
Mitch checks his chicks.
Mitch will not bring them.

Look at the truck!
It is stuck in a ditch!
Mitch must fetch Big Phil.

Mitch will **walk** Phil **around**.
Big Phil tugs and tugs.
The truck moves inch **by** inch.
Big Phil did it!

Big Phil likes to munch.
Big Phil gets a snack.
Big Phil is the best!

Safe Snakes

Mark Lehigh/Alamy

by Melissa Meyers

What helps a snake to be safe? A snake can't run. It does not have legs. What can a snake do?

Snakes can make safe nests. A snake can dig a den in sand. It will nest in logs and under plants, too.

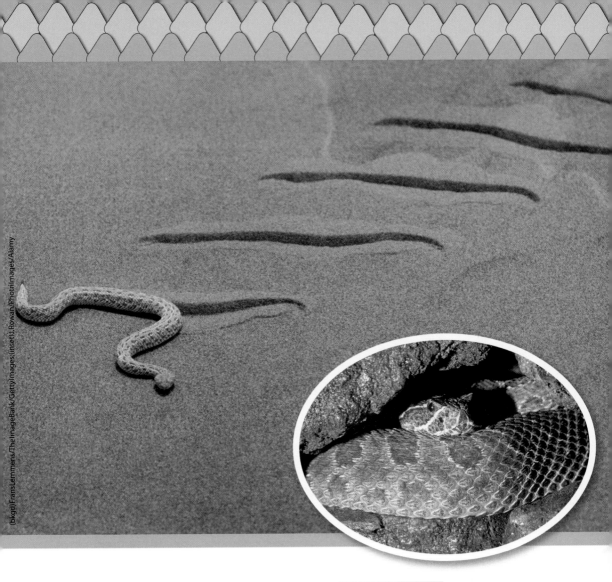

Snakes can get **away** fast. **Now** and then, a snake will slip under a rock. Then it can't be spotted.

Some snakes have scales that blend in. They look the same as land. Scales help snakes move.

14

Snakes can huff and hiss. A snake can shake at one end. A snake can flop and act as if it is dead.

Why is this snake safe **today**? It can escape. It can blend in. It can make its **way** to a safe spot.

Time to Pick Up Together

by Camille Iglesias
illustrated by Anni Matsick

This spot has lots of trash.
Let's pick it up **together**.
Then it will look **pretty**.

This is a bit of a bike.
No one can ride with it.
It will fit in a wide bag.

I will fill this bag.
I will pick up plates and cups
tossed on the **green** grass.
My bag is filled with trash.

This is a smashed kite.
This is a white pipe.
We **should** pick them up
and toss them in the bag.

The trash is in a big pile.
A truck will pick it up.
The truck will drive it away.

This spot is pretty.
Grass can **grow**.
Kids can ride by the **water**.
Good job, kids!

A Spice Cake from Vance

by Yeun Ho
illustrated by Deborah Colvin Borgo

Once **upon** a time, Vance
wished to bake his best cake.
It was not just **any** cake.
It was a fresh spice cake!

Vance placed his white
hat on his head.
He rested on the edge.
He added spice **from** a box.

28

Next, Vance chopped nuts.
He diced nine dates.
He added nuts and dates!

Vance danced on the edge.
Then he sliced and diced.
He added fresh things.
His cake looked quite good.

Vance mixed and mixed.
Then he got his cake mix in
its pan.
The next stage was baking.

Then Vance iced his cake.
He cut a nice slice.
It was a good cake.
Vance felt **so happy**!

Steve's Huge Step

by Akisha Owens
illustrated by Meryl Henderson

Steve has tunes at his home.
Steve likes **old** and new tunes.
Steve hopes to get in the
band.

Steve totes a used case to
class.
Steve waves at Mom.
Mom waves back.

Steve chose a cute tune
from long **ago**.
He sits at his stand.
Steve hits all his notes.

This **boy** and **girl** check
on **how** to play notes.
It is a long song.
They can not make a mistake.

These kids hope to get in
the band too.
People who are judges will
pick the kids.

Steve made it in the band!
It is a huge step. Steve
closes his case. It is time to
get home and tell Mom.

Unit 3

Week 1 ● *Around Dad's Ranch*............ *page 1*

Word Count: 101

Decodable Words

Target Phonics Elements: Consonant Digraphs *ch, -tch, ph*

checks, chicks, ditch, fetch, hitch, inch, Mitch, Mitch's, munch, Phil, ranch

Review: *a, and, at, best, big, bring, Dad, Dad's, did, has, helps, his, in, is, it, must, not, peck, pen, snack, stuck, them, this, truck, tugs, van, will*

High-Frequency Words

around, by, many, place, walk
Review: *go, likes, look, moves, out, the, to*

Week 2 ● *Safe Snakes*............................ *page 9*

Word Count: 127

Decodable Words

Target Phonics Element: Long *a (a_e)*

escape, make, safe, same, scales, shake, snake, snakes
Review: *a, and, act, as, blend, can, can't, dead, den, dig, end, fast, flop, get, help, huff, hiss, if, in, is, it, it's, its land, legs, logs, nest, nests, not, on, plants, rock, sand, slip, spot, spotted, then, this, will, wings*

High-Frequency Words

away, now, some, today, way, why
Review: *be, does, have, look, move, one, they, to, too, under, what*

Week 3 • *Time to Pick Up Together*...................................... *page 17*

Word Count: 120

Decodable Words

Target Phonics Element: Long *i (i_e)*

bike, drive, kite, pile, pipe, ride, time, white, wide

Review: *a, and, can, cups, bag, big, bit, fill, filled, fit, grass, has, I, in, is, it, job, kids, let's, lots, on, plates, pick, smashed, spot, them, this, toss, tossed, trash, truck, up, will, with*

High-Frequency Words

green, grow, pretty, should, together, water

Review: *away, by, good, look, my, no, of, one, the, to, we*

Week 4 • *A Spice Cake from Vance* . *page 25*

Word Count: 116

Decodable Words

Target Phonics Elements: Soft *c;* Soft *g*

danced, diced, edge, iced, placed, slice, sliced, spice, stage, Vance

Review: *a, and, added, bake, baking, best, box, cake, chopped, cut, dates, felt, fresh, got, in, it, its, hat, head, his, just, mix, mixed, next, nine, not, nuts, on, pan, quite, rested, then, time, things, white, wished*

High-Frequency Words

any, from, happy, once, so, upon

Review: *good, he, looked, the, to, was*

Week 5 ● *Steve's Huge Step* .... *page 33*

Word Count: 116

Decodable Words
Target Phonics Elements: Long *o (o_e)*,
Long *u (u_e)*, Long *e (e_e)*
*chose, closes, cute, home, hope, hopes, huge, notes,
totes, tune, tunes, Steve, Steve's, used*
Review: *a, and, at, back, band, can, case, checks, class,
get, has, his, hits, in, is, it, judges, kids, likes, long, made,
make, mistake, Mom, not, on, pick, sits, song, stand,
step, tell, this, time, waves, will*

High-Frequency Words
ago, boy, girl, how, old, people
Review: *all, are, from, he, new, play, the, these, they, to,
too, who*

Decoding skills taught to date:

Phonics: Short *a;* Short *i; l*-Blends; Short *o; r*-Blends, *s*-Blends; Short *e (e, ea);* Short *u;* End Blends *nd, nk, nt, st, sk, mp;* Consonant Digraphs: *th, sh, -ng;* Consonant Digraphs *ch, -tch, wh, ph;* Long *a (a_e);* Long *i (i_e);* Soft *c;* Soft *g, dge;* Long *o (o_e);* Long *u (u_e);* Long *e (e_e)*

Structural Analysis: Inflectional Ending -*s* (plurals, verbs); Double Final Consonants; Alphabetical Order; Possessives with *'s;* Inflectional Ending -*ed;* Contractions with *'s;* Inflectional Ending -*ing;* Closed Syllables; Inflectional Ending -*es;* Contractions with *n't;* Plurals with CVC*e* Words; Inflectional Endings -*ed, -ing* with Spelling Changes; CVC*e* Syllables